HE BEST OF DAVID BOWIE

Wise Publications
London/New York/Sydney/Paris/Copenhagen/Madrid

SOUND AND VISION

Aah
Do do etc
Don't you wonder sometimes
'Bout sound and vision?

Blue, blue, electric blue
That's the colour of my room where I will live
Blue, blue

Pale blinds drawn all day
Nothing to read, nothing to say
Blue, blue

I will sit right down
Waiting for the gift of sound and vision
And I will sing
Waiting for the gift of sound and vision
Drifting into my solitude, over my head

Don't you wonder sometimes
'Bout sound and vision?

GOLDEN YEARS

Golden years, gold
Whop, whop, whop
Golden years, gold
Whop, whop, whop
Golden years, gold
Whop, whop, whop

Don't let me hear you say life's taking you nowhere, angel
Come get up my baby
Look at that sky, life's begun
Nights are warm and the days are young
Come get up my baby
There's my baby, lost that's all
Once I'm begging you save her little soul
Golden years, gold
Whop, whop, whop
Come get up my baby

Last night they loved you
Opening doors and pulling some strings, angel
Come get up my baby
In walked luck and you looked in time
Never look back, walk tall, act fine
Come get up my baby
I'll stick with you baby for a thousand years
Nothing's gonna touch you in these golden years, gold

Golden years, gold
Whop, whop, whop
Come get up my baby

Some of these days and it won't be long
Gonna drive back down where you once belonged
In the back of a dream car twenty foot long
Don't cry my sweet don't break my heart
Doing alright but you gotta get smart
Wish upon wish upon, day upon day
I'll believe oh Lord, I'll believe all the way
Run for the shadows. Run for the shadows
Run for the shadows in these golden years

Don't let me hear you say life's taking you nowhere, angel
Come get up my baby
Run for the shadows. Run for the shadows
Run for the shadows in these golden years
I'll stick with you baby for a thousand years
Nothing's gonna touch you in these golden years, gold

Golden years, gold
Whop, whop, whop

FAME

Fame makes a man take things over
Fame lets him loose, hard to swallow
Fame puts you there where things are hollow
Fame
It's not your brain it's just the flame
That burns your change to keep you insane
Fame

Do be da be da de etc.

Fame, what you like is in the limo
Fame, what you get is no tomorrow
Fame, what you need you have to borrow
Fame
Fame, "Mine, it's mine!" is just his line
To bind your time, it drives you to crime
Fame

Is it any wonder I reject you first?
Fame, fame, fame, fame
Is it any wonder you're too cool to fool?
Fame
Fame, bully for you, chilly for me
Gotta get a raincheck on pain
Fame

Fame
Fame, what's your name?

YOUNG AMERICANS

They pulled in just behind the bridge
He lays her down, he frowns
"Gee my life's a funny thing, am I still too young?"

He kissed her then and there
She took his ring, took his babies
It took him minutes, took her nowhere
Heaven knows she'd have taken anything

All night
She wants the young American
Young American, young American
She wants the young American
All right
But she wants the young American

All the way from Washington
Her bread-winner begs off the bathroom floor
"We live for just these twenty years
Do we have to die for the fifty more?"

All night
He wants the young American
Young American, young American
He wants the young American
All right
Well he wants the young American

Do you remember your President Nixon?
Do you remember the bills you have to pay
Or even yesterday?

You ain't a pimp and you ain't a hustler
A pimp's got a Cadi and a lady got a Chrysler
Black's got respect and white's got a soul train
Mama's got cramps and look at your hands ache

I heard the news today oh boy
I got a suite and you got defeat
Ain't there a man who can say no more?
And ain't there a woman I can sock on the jaw?

And ain't there a child I can hold without judging?
And ain't there a pen that will write before they die?
Ain't you proud that you've still got faces?
Ain't there one damn song that can make me break down and cry?

All night
I want the young American
Young American, young American
I want the young American
All right
I want the young American
Young American

JOHN, I'M ONLY DANCING (AGAIN)

(Dancing) I'm having so much love
(Dancing) Too bad my back had gone
(Dancing) Boogie down with daddy now
I'd give my house in the country
If you slept less than funky

(Music) I'm dancing in the street
(Ooh music) I've torn my shoes from my feet
(Romancing) It's got me dirty and sweet
It's got you reeling and rocking
Won't you let me slam my thing in

(Falling) I think it's all I can do
(Falling) To stop me feeling it too
(Ooh falling) Give a little
Take a little, give a little back
Jumping John the great goose has gone
Got a lion on my hand, Charlie on my back

(John) I'm only dancing
(She turns me on) I'm only dancing
(She turns me on, don't get me wrong)
I'm only dancing, mm
I'm only dancing, mm

(Dancing) Have you heard the news?
(Dancing) President has got the blues
(Dancing) I tell you confidently
If he gives it to you
He'd better take it from me

(Sad sad) I'll pick up your bones
(Sad sad) Leave the numbers alone
(Sad sad) Get off your telephone
Look at people in the eye, tell 'em "My, oh my"
Let your backbone slide while you whistle and cry

(John) I'm only dancing etc.

WILD IS THE WIND

Love me, love me
Love me, love me, say you do
Let me fly away with you
For my love is like the wind
And wild is the wind
Wild is the wind

Give me more than one caress
Satisfy this hungriness
Let the wind blow through your heart
Oh wild is the wind
Wild is the wind

You touch me
I hear the sound of mandolins
You kiss me
With your kiss my life begins
You're Spring to me
All things to me
Don't you know you're life itself

Like the leaf clings to the tree
Oh, my darling cling to me
For we're like the creatures of the wind
Wild is the wind
Wild is the wind

You touch me etc.

CAN YOU HEAR ME

Once we were lovers, can they understand?
Closer than others, I was your, I was your man
Don't talk of heartaches, ooh I remember them all
And I'm checking you out one day
To see if I'm faking it all

Can you hear me?
Can you feel me inside?
Show your love
Take it in right
Take it in right

There's been many others ooh ooh so many times
Sixty new cities, so what do I
What do I find?
I want love so badly, I want you most of all
You know it's harder to take it from any-one
It's harder to fall
Can you hear me call?

Can you (hear me?)
Can you (feel me inside?)
Show me your love (love, love)
Take it in right
Take it in right

Well can you hear me? (yeah)
Can you feel me inside? (I do)
Show me love, show your sweet, sweet love
Show me your love
Take it in right
Take it in right yeah
Baby take it in right to your love life

Take it in right
Take it in right, right to your love life

KNOCK ON WOOD

I don't want to lose the good thing that I've got
If I do I will surely, I will lose a lot
For your love is better than any other love I've known
It's like thunder, lightning
The way you love me is fright'ning
I'd better knock on wood Baby!

I'm not superstitious about you but I can't take a chance
You got me spinning, baby spinning in a trance
But your love is better than any other love I've known
It's like thunder, lightning
The way you love me is fright'ning
You'd better knock on wood

It's no secret that that woman fills my lovin' cup
And she see to it that I get enough
And her love is better than any other love I've known
It's like thunder, lightning
The way you love me is fright'ning
I'd better knock on wood Baby!

Guess you'd better knock on wood etc.

TVC 15

Oh oh oh etc.
Up ev'ry ev'ning 'bout half eight or nine
I give my complete attention to a very good friend of mine
He's quadrophonic he's a, he's got more channels
So hologramic, oh my TVC one five

I brought my baby home she, she sat around forlorn
She saw my TVC one five, baby's gone
She, she crawled right in my, my, my, she crawled right in my
So hologramic, oh my TVC one five
Oh, so demonic, oh my TVC one five

One of these night I may just jump down that rainbow way
Be with my baby, then we'll spend some time together
So hologramic, oh my TVC one five
My baby's in there someplace love's rating in the sky
So hologramic, oh my TVC one five

Transition
Oh my TVC one five

Maybe if I pray every each night I sit there pleading
"Send back my dream test baby
She's my main feature"
My TVC one five he, he just stares back unblinking
So hologramic, oh my TVC one five

One of these nights etc.

IT'S HARD TO BE A SAINT IN THE CITY

I had skin like leather and the diamond-hard look of a cobra
I was born blue and weathered but I burst just like a supernova
I could walk like Brando right into the sun and dance just like a Casanova
With my black-jack and jacket and my hair slicked sweet
Silver studs on my duds just like a Harley in heat
When I strut down the street I can hear its heartbeat
The sisters fell back and said "Don't that man look pretty"
The cripple on the corner cried out "Hey, nickels for your pity"
Them gasoline boys downtown, they sure talk gritty
It's so hard to be a saint in the city

I was the king of the alley, mama, I could talk some trash
I was the Prince of the Paupers, crowned downtown at the Beggars' Bash
I was a pimp's main prophet, I kept everything cool
Just a back-street gambler with the luck to lose
And when the heat came down it was left on the ground, and the
Devil appeared to me like Jesus through the steam in the street
And showed me a hand that even the cops couldn't beat
And I felt his hot breath on my neck as I drove into the heat
And it's so hard to be a saint when you're just a poor boy out on the street

And the sages of the subway sit just like the living dead
As the tracks clack out the rhythm, the eyes fixed straight ahead
They ride the line of balancing, hold on by just a thread
But it's too hot in these tunnels, you can get hit up by the heat
When you get up to get out at your next stop
But they push you back down in your seat
And your heart starts beating faster as you struggle to your feet
Then you're out of that hole, back on the street

And them south-side sisters, they sure look pretty
And the cripple on the corner cries out "Nickels for your pity"
And them downtown boys, they sure talk gritty
It's so hard to be a saint in the city

1984

Someday they will get you, now you must agree
The times they are a-telling and the changing isn't free
You've read it in the tea leaves and the tracks are on TV
Beware the savage lure of 1984

They'll split your pretty cranium and fill it full of air
And tell you that you're eighty, but brother you won't care
You'll be shooting up on anything, tomorrow's never there
Beware the savage lure of 1984

Come see, come see, remember me?
We played out an all night movie role
You said it would last
But I guess we enrolled in 1984
(Who could ask for more) 1984

I'm looking for a vehicle, I'm looking for a ride
I'm looking for a party, I'm looking for a side
I'm looking for the treason that I knew in '65
Beware the savage lure of 1984

Come see etc.

LOOK BACK IN ANGER

"You know who I am" he said
The speaker was an angel
He coughed and shook his crumpled wings
Closed his eyes and moved his lips
"It's time we should be going"

(Waiting so long, I've been waiting so, waiting so)
Look back in anger, driven by the night, till you come
(Waiting so long, I've been waiting so, waiting so)
Look back in anger, see it in my eyes, till you come

No one seemed to hear him
So he leafed through a magazine
And yawning rubbed the sleep away
Very sane he seemed to me

(Waiting so long, I've been waiting so, waiting so) etc.

THE SECRET LIFE OF ARABIA

The secret life of Arabia
Secret secrets never seen
Secret secrets ever green

I was running at the speed of light from morning's thoughts and fantasies
Then I saw your eyes at the cross fades
Secret secrets never seen
Secret secrets ever green

The secret life of Arabia
Never here never seen
Secret life ever green

The secret life of Arabia
You must see the movie, the sand in my eyes
I walk through a desert song when the heroine dies

Arabia (secret secret) etc.

The secret life of Arabia etc.

DJ

I'm home lost my job and incurably ill
You think this is easy, realism
I've got a girl out there I suppose
I think she's dancing
Feel like Dan Dare lies down
I think she's dancing, what do I know?

I am a DJ, I am what I play
Can't turn around no, can't turn around no
Oh ooh ooh!
I am a DJ, I am what I play
Can't turn around no, can't turn around no
Oh no!
I am a DJ, I am what I play
I've got believers, believing me

One more weekend
Of lights and evening faces
Fast food, living nostalgia
Humble pie or bitter fruit

I am a DJ etc.

I am a DJ, I am what I play
Can't turn around no, can't turn around
I am a DJ, I am what I play
Can't turn around no, can't turn around
I am a DJ, I am what I play
Can't turn around no, can't turn around
Time flies when you're having fun
Break his heart. Break her heart
He used to be my boss and here he is a puppet dancer
I am the DJ and I've got believers

I've got believers
I've got believers
I've got believers in me
I've got believers
I've got believers
I am a DJ, I am what I play
I am a DJ

BEAUTY AND THE BEAST

Weaving down a by-road, singing the song
That's my kind of high-road gone wrong
(My my) smile at least
You can't say no to the Beauty and the Beast

Something in the night, something in the day
Nothing is wrong but darling something's in the way
There's slaughter in the air, protest on the wind
Someone else inside me, someone could get skinned, how?
(My, my) someone fetch a priest
You can't say no to the Beauty and the Beast. Darling

(My, my) you can't say no to the Beauty and the Beast. (Liebling)
(My, my) you can't say no to the Beauty and the Beast
I wanted to believe me, I wanted to be good
I wanted no distractions. Like every good boy should
(My, my)

Nothing will corrupt us, nothing will compete
Thank God heaven left us, standing on our feet
My, my Beauty and the Beast
Just Beauty and the Beast
(You can't so say no to the Beauty and the Beast)
(Darling)

BREAKING GLASS

Baby I've been breaking glass in your room again. Listen
Don't look at the carpet, I drew something awful on it. See

You're such a wonderful person but you got problems. Oh!
I'll never touch you

BOYS KEEP SWINGING

Heaven loves ya
The clouds part for ya
Nothing stands in your way when you're a boy
Clothes always fit ya
Life is a pop of the cherry when you're a boy

(When you're a boy) you can wear a uniform
(When you're a boy) other boys check you out
(You get a girl) these are your fav'rite things
(When you're a boy)

(Boys) (Boys)
(Boys keep swinging, boys always work it out)

Uncage the colours, unfurl the flag
Luck just kissed you "hello", when you're a boy
They'll never clone ya
You're always first on the line when you're a boy

(When you're a boy) you can buy a home of your own
(When you're a boy) Learn to drive and ev'rything
(You'll get your share when you're a boy)

(Boys) (Boys)
(Boys keep swinging, boys always work it out)

HEROES

I, I wish you could swim
Like the dolphins, like dolphins can swim
Though nothing, nothing will keep us together
We can beat them for ever and ever
Oh we can be heroes just for one day

I, I will be King
And you, you will be Queen
Though nothing will drive them away
We can be heroes, just for one day
We can be us, just for one day

I, I can remember (I remember)
Standing by the wall (by the wall)
And the guns shot above our heads (over our heads)
And we kissed as though nothing could fall (nothing could fall)
And the shame was on the other side
Oh we can beat them for ever and ever
Then we could be heroes just for one day
We can be heroes

SOUND AND VISION

Words & Music by David Bowie

Do do do do___ do do do do do do do___ do do do___

do.___

Don't you won-der some-times___

'bout sound and vi-sion?___

Blue, blue.

I will sit right down, wait-ing for the gift of sound and

vi - sion.___ And I will sing,

wait-ing for the gift of sound and vi - sion.___ Drift - ing__ in-

GOLDEN YEARS

Words & Music by David Bowie

14

D.%. al Coda

Run for the sha - dows.___ Run for the sha - dows in these gold - en years.___

⊕ Coda

Repeat ad lib. to fade

Gold - en years,___ gold,_____ whop, whop, whop.

%:
Don't let me hear you say life's taking you nowhere, angel
Come get up my baby.
Run for the shadows, run for the shadows
Run for the shadows in these golden years
I'll stick with you baby for a thousand years
Nothing's gonna touch you in these golden years
Gold.

Golden years *etc*.

FAME

Words & Music by David Bowie, John Lennon & Carlos Alomar

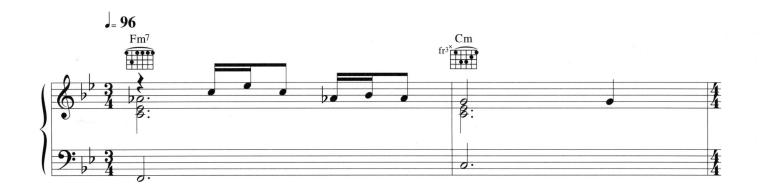

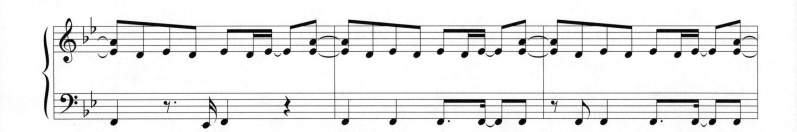

1. Fame___ makes a man___ take things ov - er. Fame___ lets him
(Verses 2 & 3 see block lyrics)

loose, hard to swal-low. Fame___ puts you there___where things are hol - low.

fame,   fame,   fame,   fame,   fame,   fame,   fame,   fame,   fame,   fame,   fame.

Repeat to fade

Fame,   what's your name?—

Verse 2:

Fame, what you like is in the limo
Fame, what you get is no tomorrow
Fame, what you need you have to borrow
Fame
Fame, "Mine, it's mine!" is just his line
To bind your time, it drives you to crime
Fame.

Verse 3:

Is it any wonder I reject you first?
Fame, fame, fame, fame
Is it any wonder you're too cool to fool?
Fame
Fame, bully for you, chilly for me
Gotta get a raincheck on pain
Fame.

YOUNG AMERICANS

Words & Music by David Bowie

4. You ain't a pimp and you ain't a hus - tler. A pimp's got a Ca - di and a la - dy got a Chry - sler.

Black's got re - spect and whites's got a soul — train. Ma - ma's got cramps and look at your hands — ache.

5. (I heard the news — to - day — oh boy) I got a suite and you got de - feat. —

Ain't there a man — who can say no more? — And ain't there a wo - man I can sock on the jaw? — 6. And

(- can.)   (Young A - me - ri - can, young A - me - ri - can, I want the young_ A - me - ri - can.

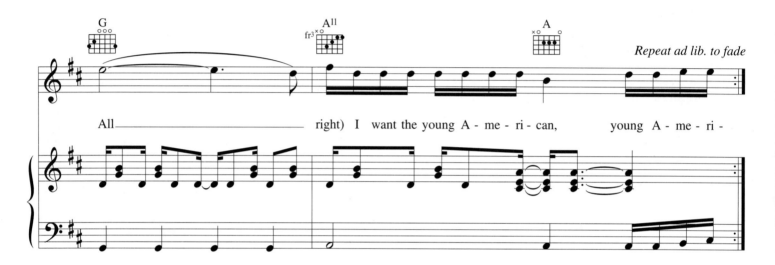

Repeat ad lib. to fade

All_____ right) I want the young A - me - ri - can,   young A - me - ri -

Verse 3:
All the way from Washington
Her bread-winner begs off the bathroom floor
"We live for just these twenty years
Do we have to die for the fifty more?"

All night *etc.*

JOHN, I'M ONLY DANCING (AGAIN)

Words & Music by David Bowie

1. (Dan-cing)   I'm hav-ing   so much love.

(Dan - cing) Too bad my back had gone. (Dan - cing) Boo - gie down with

dad - dy now. I'd give my house in the coun - try if you slept less than fun - ky.

2. (Mu - sic) I'm danc - ing in the street. (Ooh_____ mu - sic) I've torn my
(Verses 4 & 5 see block lyric)

shoes from my feet.____ (Ro - man - cing) It's got me dir - ty and sweet. It's got you

reel - ing and rock - ing, won't you let me slam my thing in. 3. (Fall - ing) I think it's

all I can do,___ (Fall - ing) to stop me feel - ing it too.___ (Ooh___

fall - ing) Give a lit - tle, take a lit - tle, give a lit - tle back.

Jump - ing John___ the great goose has gone, got a li - on on my hand, Char - lie on my back.

Verse 4:
(Dancing) Have you heard the news?
(Dancing) President has got the blues
(Dancing) I tell you confidently
If he gives it to you he'd better take it from me.

Verse 5:
(Sad sad) I'll pick up your bones
(Sad sad) Leave the numbers alone
(Sad sad) Get off your telephone
Look at people in the eye, tell 'em "My, oh my"
Let your backbone slide while you whistle and cry.

John *etc.*

CAN YOU HEAR ME

Words & Music by David Bowie

Once we were lov-ers,___ can they un-der-stand?

from a-ny-one.

It's hard-er to fall.

Can you hear me call?

Can

you (hear me?)

Can you (feel me in-side?)

Show me your love. (Love, love)

WILD IS THE WIND

Words & Music by Dimitri Tiomkin & Ned Washington

and wild is the wind. Wild is the wind.

2. Give me more than one ca-
(Verse 3 & 𝄋 see block lyric)

-ress. Sa-tis-fy this

hun - gri - ness. Let the

Verse 3 & %:
Like the leaf clings to the tree
Oh, my darling cling to me
For we're like creatures of the wind
Wild is the wind
Wild is the wind.

You touch me *etc.*

KNOCK ON WOOD

Words & Music by Eddie Floyd & Steve Cropper

knock,   knock, knock on   wood.—   Guess you'd bet-ter   knock, knock.   Oh—

—   no ba-by!   Knock on wood. Woo!

Verse 2:
I'm not superstitious about you
But I can't take a chance
You got me spinning, baby
Spinning in a trance
But your love is better
Than any other love I've known
It's like thunder, lightning
The way you love me is frightening
You'd better knock on wood.

Verse 3:
It's no secret that that woman
Fills my lovin' cup
And she sees to it
That I get enough
And her love is better
Than any other love I've known
It's like thunder, lightning
The way you love me is frightening
I'd better knock on wood.
Baby!

TVC 15

Words & Music by David Bowie

five,___ ba - by's gone.___ She, she crawled right in my, my, my,

she crawled right in my, so ho-lo-gram-ic, oh my T V C one five.

1.

Oh, so de - mon - ic, oh my T V C one five.

2, 3.

T V C one five. Tran - - - si - tion.

gliss.

Trans - mis - sion. Tran - si - tion.

Trans - mis - sion.

Oh my T V C one five, oh, oh, T V C one five.

Oh my T V C one five, oh, oh

Verse 3 & 𝄋:

One of these nights I may just
Jump down that rainbow way
Be with my baby, then
We'll spend some time together
So hologramic, oh my TVC one five
My baby's in there someplace
Love's rating in the sky
So hologramic, oh my TVC one five.

Transition *etc.*

Verse 4:

Maybe if I pray every
Each night I sit there pleading
"Send back my dream test baby
She's my main feature"
My TVC one five he
He just stares back unblinking
So hologramic, oh my TVC one five.

One of these nights *etc.*

1984

Words & Music by David Bowie

1. Some-day they will get you, now you must a-gree. The times they are a-tell-ing—— and the
(Verses 2 & 3 see block lyrics)

Nine - teen eigh - ty four._____

Nine - teen eigh - ty four._____

Verse 2:
They'll split your pretty cranium
And fill it full of air
And tell you that you're eighty
But brother you won't care
You'll be shooting up on anything
Tomorrow's never there
Beware the savage lure
Of 1984.

Come see *etc.*

Verse 3:
I'm looking for a vehicle
I'm looking for a ride
I'm looking for a party
I'm looking for a side
I'm looking for the treason
That I knew in '65
Beware the savage lure
Of 1984.

Come see *etc.*

THE SECRET LIFE OF ARABIA

Words & Music by David Bowie, Carlos Alomar & Brian Eno

ne - ver seen.___ Se - cret se - crets ev - er green.___

The___ se - - - cret life___ of___ A -

- ra - bia.___ Ne - ver here ne - ver

IT'S HARD TO BE
A SAINT IN THE CITY

Words & Music by Bruce Springsteen

1. I had

skin like lea - ther   and the dia-mond-hard look of __ a co - bra.

(Verse 2 see block lyric)

I was born blue __ and wea-thered   but I burst just like __ a su-per-

-no-va.   I could   walk like __ Bran - do right in-

-to __ the sun   and dance just like a Ca - sa - no - va.

With my black-jack and jack-et and my hair slicked sweet, sil-ver studs on my duds just like a Har-ley in heat. When I strut down the street— I can hear its heart-beat.— The sis-ters fell back and said "Don't that man look pret-ty." (℁ see block lyric) The crip-ple on the cor-ner cried out "hey, nick-els for your pi-ty." Them

Verse 2:

I was the king of the alley, mama, I could talk some trash
I was the Prince of the Paupers, crowned down-town at the Beggars' Bash
I was a pimp's main prophet, I kept everything cool
Just a back-street gambler with the luck to lose
And when the heat came down it was left on the ground, and the
Devil appeared to me like Jesus through the steam in the street, and
Showed me a hand that even the cops couldn't beat
And I felt his hot breath on my neck as I dove into the heat, and
It's so hard to be a saint when you're just a poor boy out on the street.

℅:

And them south-side sisters, they sure look pretty
And the cripple on the corner cries out "Nickels for your pity"
And them down-town boys, they sure talk gritty
It's so hard to be a saint in the city.

LOOK BACK IN ANGER

Words & Music by David Bowie & Brian Eno

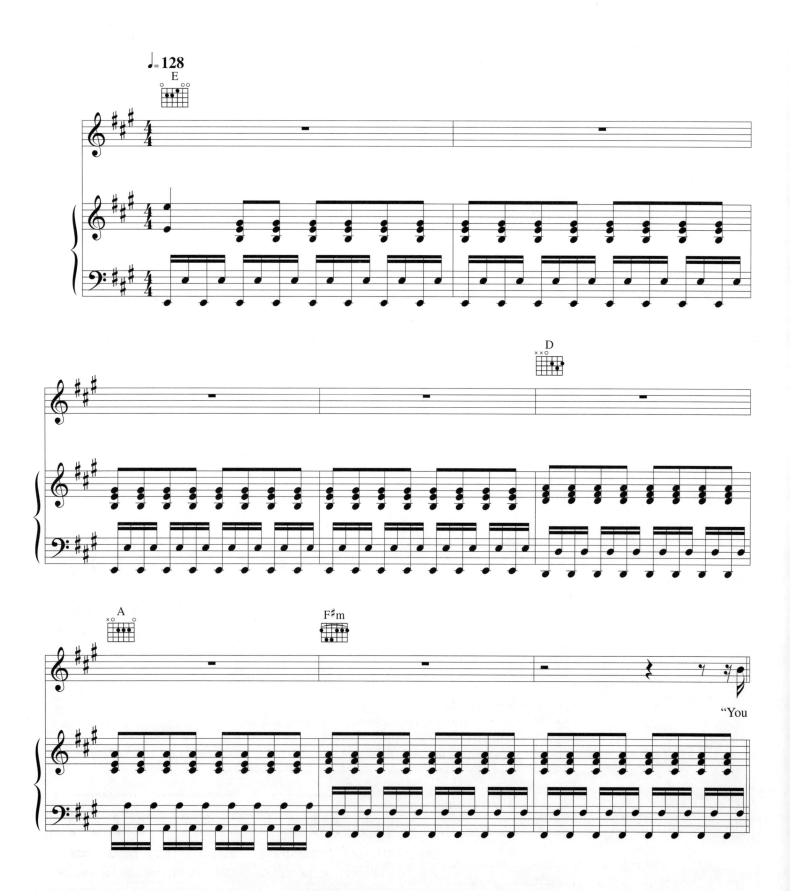

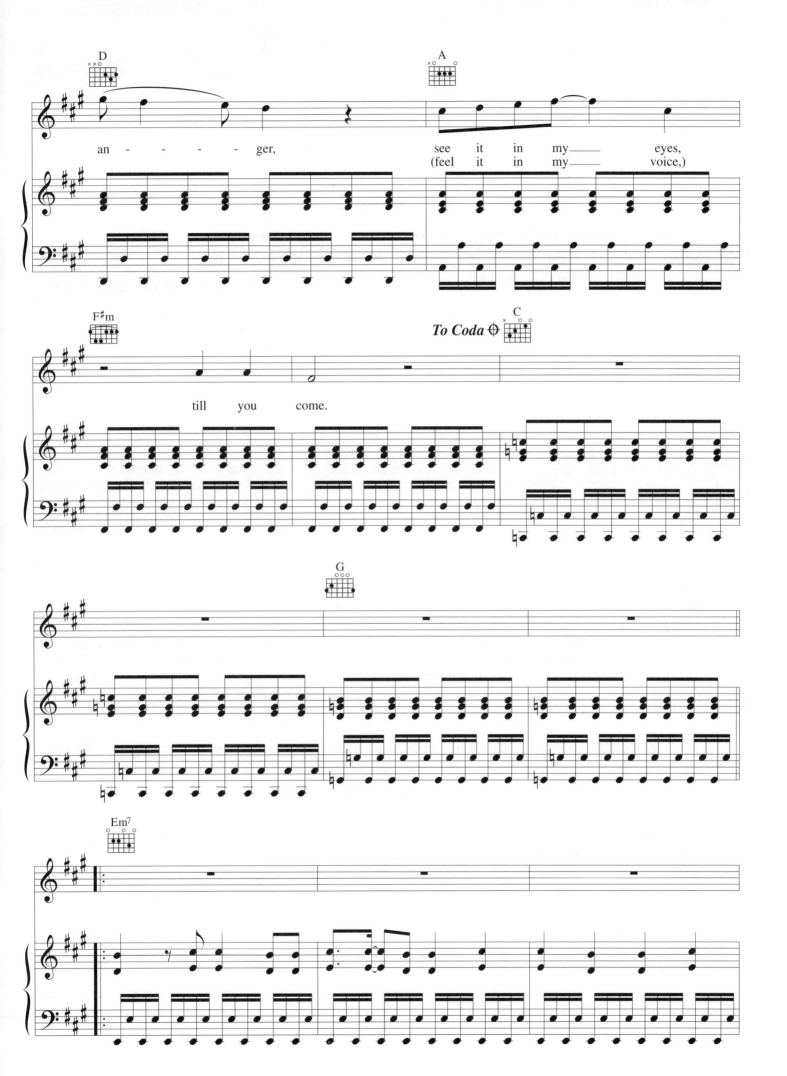

DJ

Words & Music by David Bowie, Carlos Alomar & Brian Eno

Lyrics:
1. I'm home lost my job, and in-cu-ra-bly ill. You think this
(Verse 2 see block lyric)

Verse 2:
One more weekend
Of lights and evening faces
Fast food, living nostalgia
Humble pie or bitter fruit.

I am a D.J. *etc.*

BEAUTY AND THE BEAST

Words & Music by David Bowie

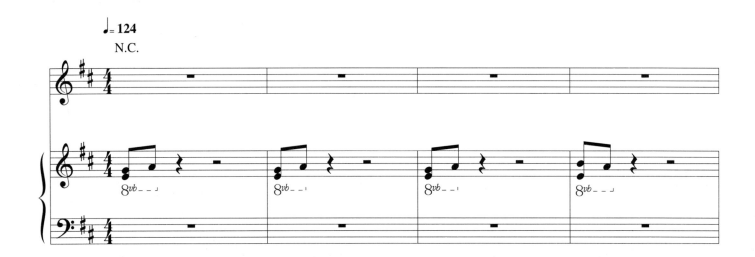

Beau - ty and the Beast.

Some-thing in the night, some-thing in the day. No-thing is wrong— but darl- ing

some-thing's in the way. There's slaugh- ter in the air, pro - test on the wind.

Some-one else in-side me, some-one could get skinned, how?

(My, my.)— Some-one fetch a priest. You can't say no— to the

Beau-ty and the Beast. Darl - - ing.

(My,   my.)—   You   can't   say   no— to the

Beau ty   and   the Beast.   (Lieb - - ling)

(My,   my.)—

No-thing will cor-rupt us, no-thing will com-pete. Thank God hea-ven left us,

stand-ing on our feet. My, my.— Beau-ty and the

Beast.
(My, my.)— Just Beau-ty and the Beast.
(You can't say no— to the

Beau - ty and the Beast.) (Dar - ling.)

D/A   A¹¹

A7

Repeat to fade

(My, my.) (My)

BREAKING GLASS

Words & Music by David Bowie, Dennis Davis & George Murray

Ba - by I've been break-ing glass in your
(2° Instrumental)

room a-gain. Lis- ten.

Don't look at the car-pet, I drew some - thing

aw- ful on it. See.

You're such a won-der-ful

per-son

but you got

prob-lems.

Oh!

I'll ne-ver touch you.

100

BOYS KEEP SWINGING

Words & Music by David Bowie & Brian Eno

(Boys)

(Boys)

(Boys keep swing-ing,

boys al - ways— work it out.)— Un-cage the col-ours,
(Gtr. solo on D.℠.)

un-furl the flag.   Luck just kissed__ you__ "hel-lo,"__

when you're a boy.__

They'll ne-ver clone__ ya.   You're al-ways first   on the line__

when you're a boy.__   (When you're a   boy.)_

HEROES

Words & Music by David Bowie & Brian Eno

beat them

for ev - er and ev - er.

Oh we can be he - roes

just for one day.—

1.

2.

I,

I can re - mem — ber (I re - mem-

Verse 2:
I, I will be King
And you, you will be Queen
Though nothing will drive them away
We can be heroes, just for one day
We can be us, just for one day.

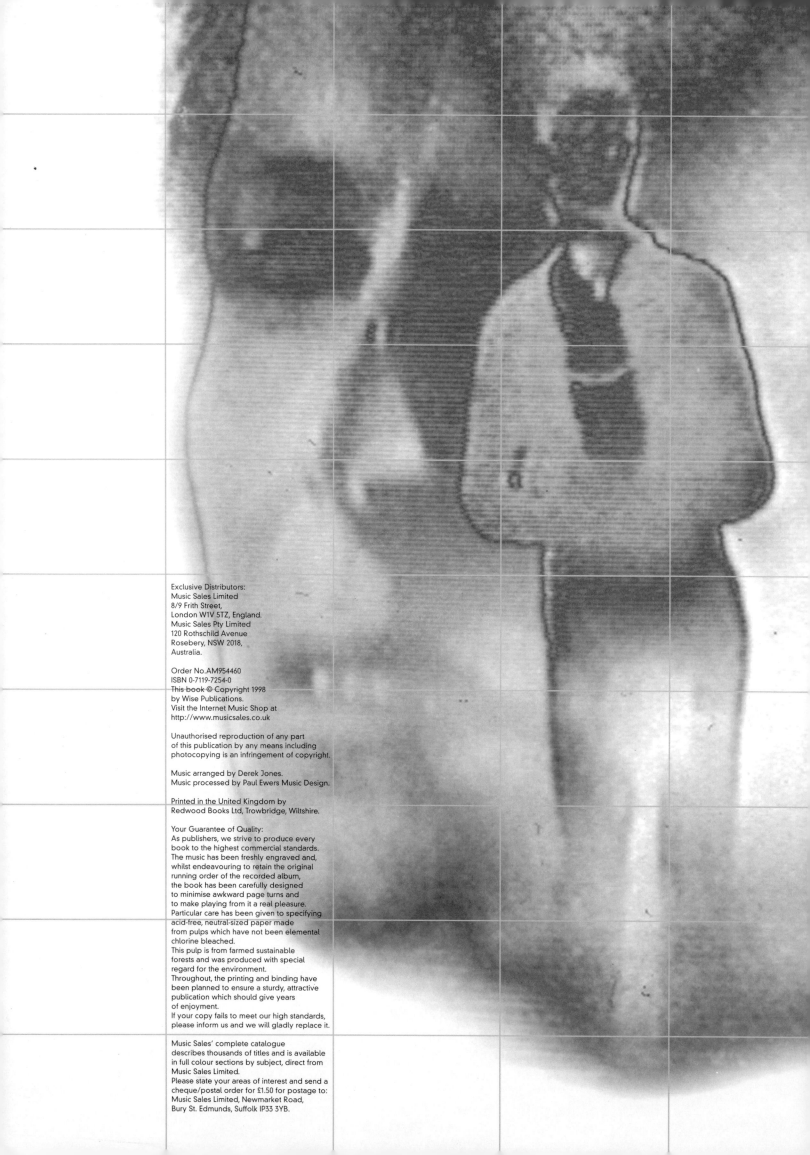

Exclusive Distributors:
Music Sales Limited
8/9 Frith Street,
London W1V 5TZ, England.
Music Sales Pty Limited
120 Rothschild Avenue
Rosebery, NSW 2018,
Australia.

Order No.AM954460
ISBN 0-7119-7254-0
This book © Copyright 1998
by Wise Publications.
Visit the Internet Music Shop at
http://www.musicsales.co.uk

Music arranged by Derek Jones.
Music processed by Paul Ewers Music Design.

Printed in the United Kingdom by
Redwood Books Ltd, Trowbridge, Wiltshire.

Your Guarantee of Quality:
As publishers, we strive to produce every
book to the highest commercial standards.
The music has been freshly engraved and,
whilst endeavouring to retain the original
running order of the recorded album,
the book has been carefully designed
to minimise awkward page turns and
to make playing from it a real pleasure.
Particular care has been given to specifying
acid-free, neutral-sized paper made
from pulps which have not been elemental
chlorine bleached.
This pulp is from farmed sustainable
forests and was produced with special
regard for the environment.
Throughout, the printing and binding have
been planned to ensure a sturdy, attractive
publication which should give years
of enjoyment.
If your copy fails to meet our high standards,
please inform us and we will gladly replace it.

Music Sales' complete catalogue
describes thousands of titles and is available
in full colour sections by subject, direct from
Music Sales Limited.
Please state your areas of interest and send a
cheque/postal order for £1.50 for postage to:
Music Sales Limited, Newmarket Road,
Bury St. Edmunds, Suffolk IP33 3YB.